in the countryside activity book

Published by Collins
An imprint of HarperCollins Publishers
Westerhill Road
Bishopbriggs
Glasgow G64 2QT
www.harpercollins.co.uk

© HarperCollins Publishers 2020

Collins® is a registered trademark of HarperCollins Publishers Ltd
i-SPY® is a registered trademark of Michelin.

All rights reserved. No part of this publication may be reproduced, stored in a retrieval system, or transmitted, in any form or by any means, electronic, mechanical, photocopying, recording or otherwise without the prior permission in writing of the publisher and copyright owners.

The contents of this publication are believed correct at the time of printing. Nevertheless the publisher can accept no responsibility for errors or omissions, changes in the detail given or for any expense or loss thereby caused.

HarperCollins does not warrant that any website mentioned in this title will be provided uninterrupted, that any website will be error-free, that defects will be corrected, or that the website or the server that makes it available are free of viruses or bugs. For full terms and conditions please refer to the site terms provided on the website.

A catalogue record for this book is available from the British Library.

ISBN 9780008392864

10 9 8 7 6 5 4 3 2 1

Printed in China

Images © Shutterstock.com

i-SPY

in the countryside activity book

SPY IT! SOLVE IT!

Contents

How to use your i-SPY activity book

Work your way through the puzzles and activities in any order you like - you don't have to start at the beginning.

As you go, keep your eyes peeled for the spots. If you spot it, score it by ticking the circle or star.

Items with a star are difficult to find so you'll have to search high and low to find them.

Once you've finished spotting, complete your super i-SPY certificate found at the back of the book and record your score.

Senses - touch

Feather
(sticky)

Goosegrass
(sticky)

Lichen
(flaky)

Moss
(soft)

Petals
(silky)

Raindrop
(wet)

Soil
(crumbly)

Teasel
(prickly)

There are many different textures to spot and feel when exploring the countryside. Can you find the items listed on the opposite page in the wordsearch below?

Solve it!

l	i	c	h	e	n	d	o	t	a	a	y	e
p	f	y	r	c	y	r	m	o	s	s	u	g
f	r	r	a	f	e	a	t	h	e	r	p	o
u	o	s	i	i	a	p	q	q	o	s	e	o
c	h	h	n	x	r	d	i	t	r	p	l	s
l	r	s	d	g	q	f	s	e	h	t	l	e
v	w	i	r	p	j	t	o	a	a	l	s	g
e	l	m	o	e	m	k	i	s	i	r	c	r
q	s	a	p	t	s	r	l	e	p	l	r	a
q	u	u	b	a	c	k	r	l	i	r	c	s
o	w	r	p	l	o	x	g	i	b	t	d	s
a	i	z	a	s	d	a	j	g	a	s	g	w
o	t	a	u	j	t	r	f	d	p	i	s	l

Senses - sound

Keep your eyes and ears peeled as you explore the countryside and listen out for the wonderful sounds.

Can you rearrange the letters to form the names of three loud sounds?

Spot it!

25 POINTS

Solve it!

Hint: owls make this sound.

Hint: crickets make this sound.

Hint: frogs make this sound.

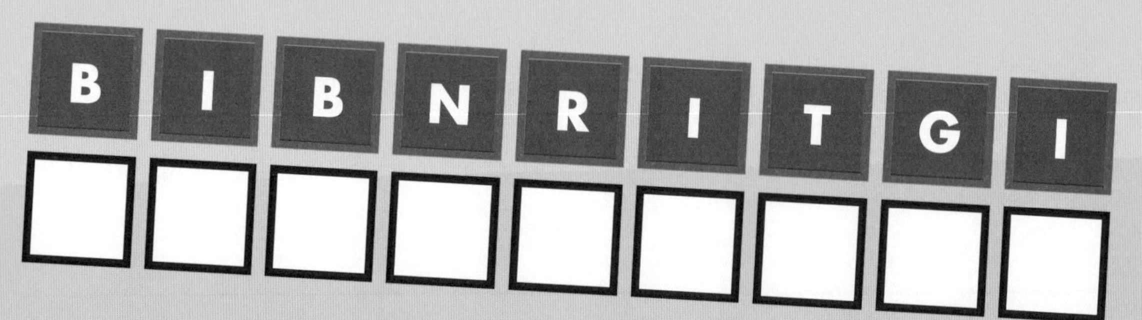

Colour me!

Senses - smell

This plant flowers in spring and fills woodlands with its strange garlic-like smell. Wild boar like to dig up the bulbs and eat them.

This wild boar is hungry! Can you guide it through the maze to reach the wild garlic bulbs?

Honeysuckle

Spot it!

○ **10 POINTS**

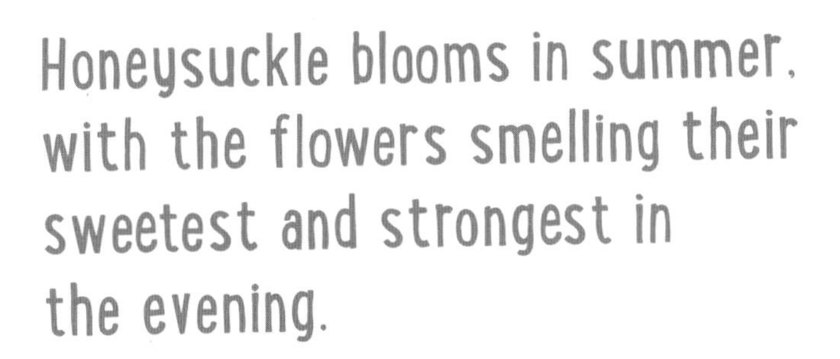

Honeysuckle blooms in summer, with the flowers smelling their sweetest and strongest in the evening.

Take a sniff around the countryside and see what else you can smell. Gorse? Fungus? Any animals? Record the details here:

Smell 1:
Smells like:

Smell 2:
Smells like:

Smell 3:
Smells like:

Write here!

Senses - taste

Blackberries come from the bramble plant, ripening in late summer when they're perfect for picking.

Can you rearrange the letters in the word wheels to reveal the names of other kinds of berries?

Blackberries

Spot it!

5 POINTS

Solve it!

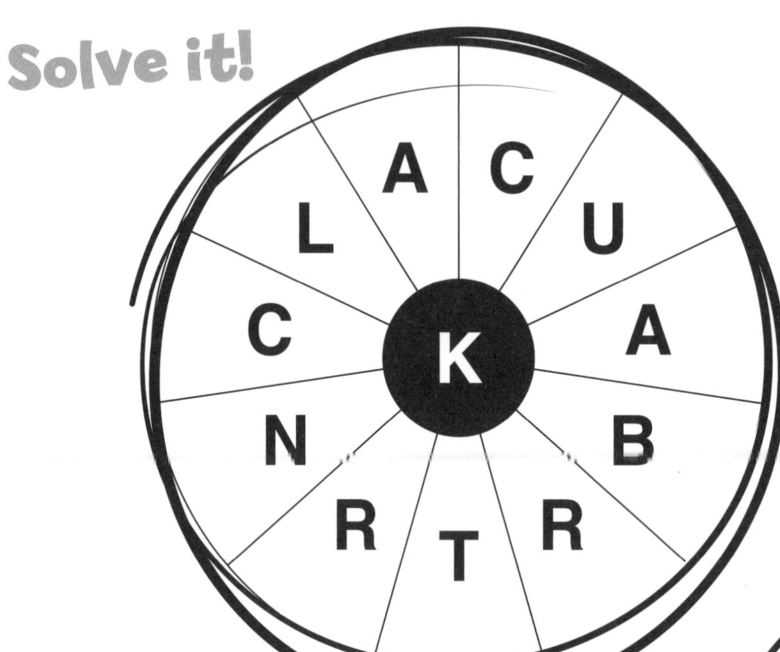

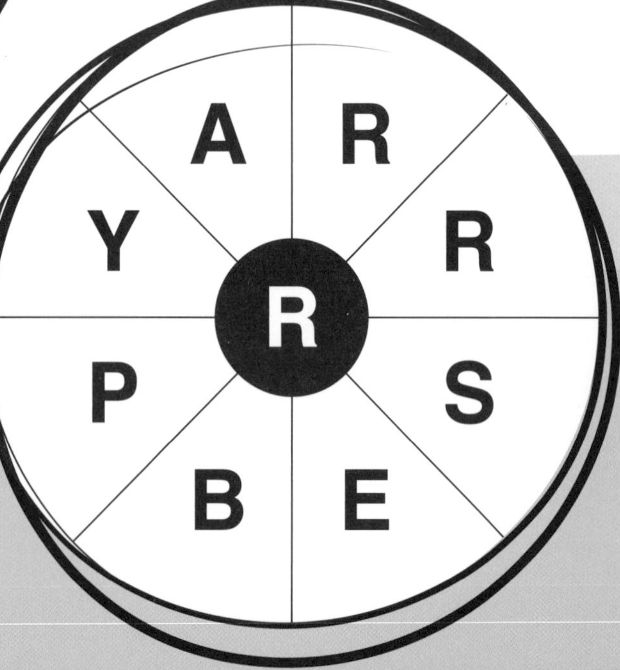

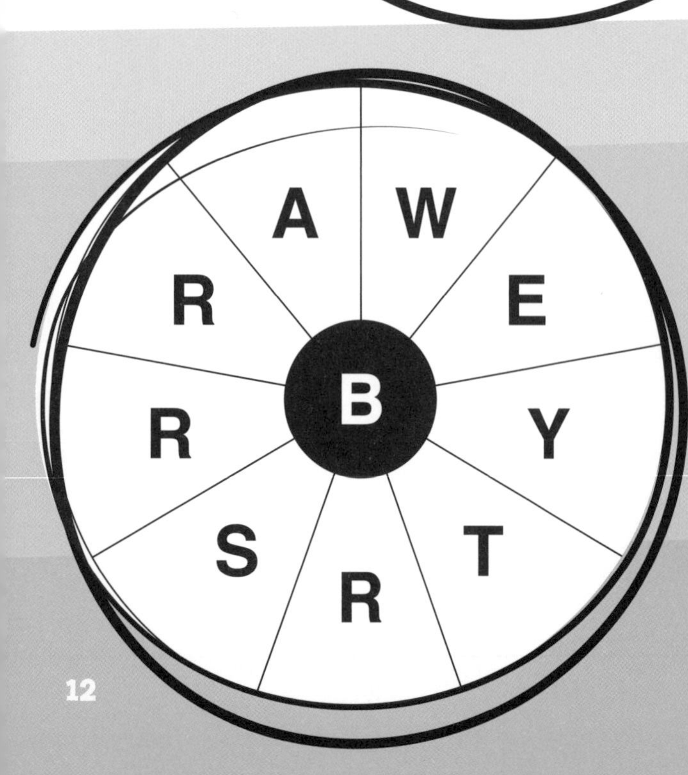

The elder tree flowers in early summer, and the blossom is commonly used to make cordial and champagne.

Elderflowers

Spot it!

10 POINTS

Colour me!

Senses - sight

Beautiful sights are all around you. Flowers, trees and leaves of all shapes, sizes and colours fill the countryside. Watch out for them changing between the seasons too.

Help bring this page to life by colouring the leaves.

Colour me!

Autumn hues

Spot it!
10
POINTS

Winter whites
Spot it!
10
POINTS

Nature's playground

Take a closer look at the trees around you – can you see any faces looking back? Knobbly growths, gnarled roots and dark animal tunnels underneath trees often look like eyes, noses, and mouths.

Found one? Take a picture and stick it below or draw a sketch.

Face in the trees

Build a den

Can you find a secret shelter hidden in the woods? Make your own with fallen branches, grass and leaves. What can you find to make it waterproof and windproof?

Draw the den you built below (or design your dream den instead!).

Spot it!

35 POINTS

Draw here!

Nature's playground

Let's play 'nature's playground' bingo! When you see or do one of the things on this bingo card, cross off the square.

Spot it!

5 POINTS

Splash in a puddle
Weave through trees
Make a tree swing
Hug a tree
Hide in the woods
Crawl through grass

Spring – minibeasts

Ant

Butterfly

Earthworm

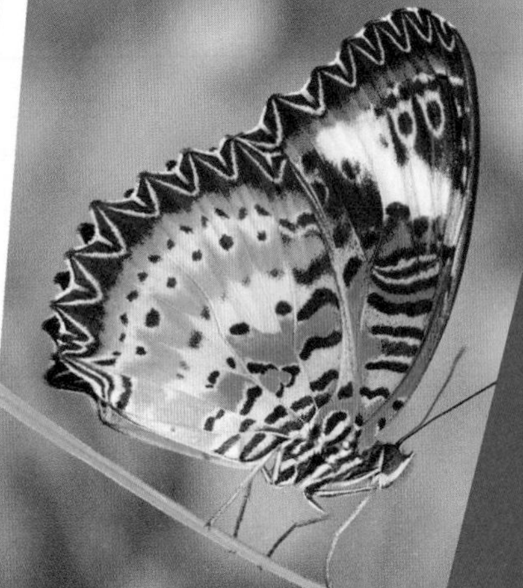

Lacewing

Ladybird

Moth

Snail

Woodlouse

Speckled wood butterfly

Spot it!

25 POINTS

How many of the spring minibeasts opposite can you find in the wordsearch below?

Solve it!

f	b	u	f	e	a	r	t	h	w	o	r	m
w	u	i	g	c	u	a	t	o	n	f	m	b
s	t	a	g	r	w	n	t	r	g	k	s	v
l	t	r	s	y	p	t	e	y	i	g	v	s
a	e	l	l	m	r	x	p	r	f	s	t	a
d	r	a	x	s	z	s	l	x	i	o	a	m
y	f	c	w	o	o	d	l	o	u	s	e	o
b	l	e	t	l	j	e	b	s	m	r	s	t
i	y	w	q	f	o	y	l	u	x	s	n	h
r	o	i	j	j	x	o	u	a	m	i	a	t
d	l	n	i	g	e	d	s	p	g	b	i	s
i	y	g	s	a	a	a	i	m	h	e	l	y
c	b	w	r	o	t	o	z	a	l	r	t	e

Spring - amphibians

Frogspawn

Look closely next time you are at a pond and you might see frogspawn. Over time frogspawn develops into tadpoles.

Can you help this little tadpole avoid the fish and get to the other side of the pond?

Spot it!

20 POINTS

Solve it!

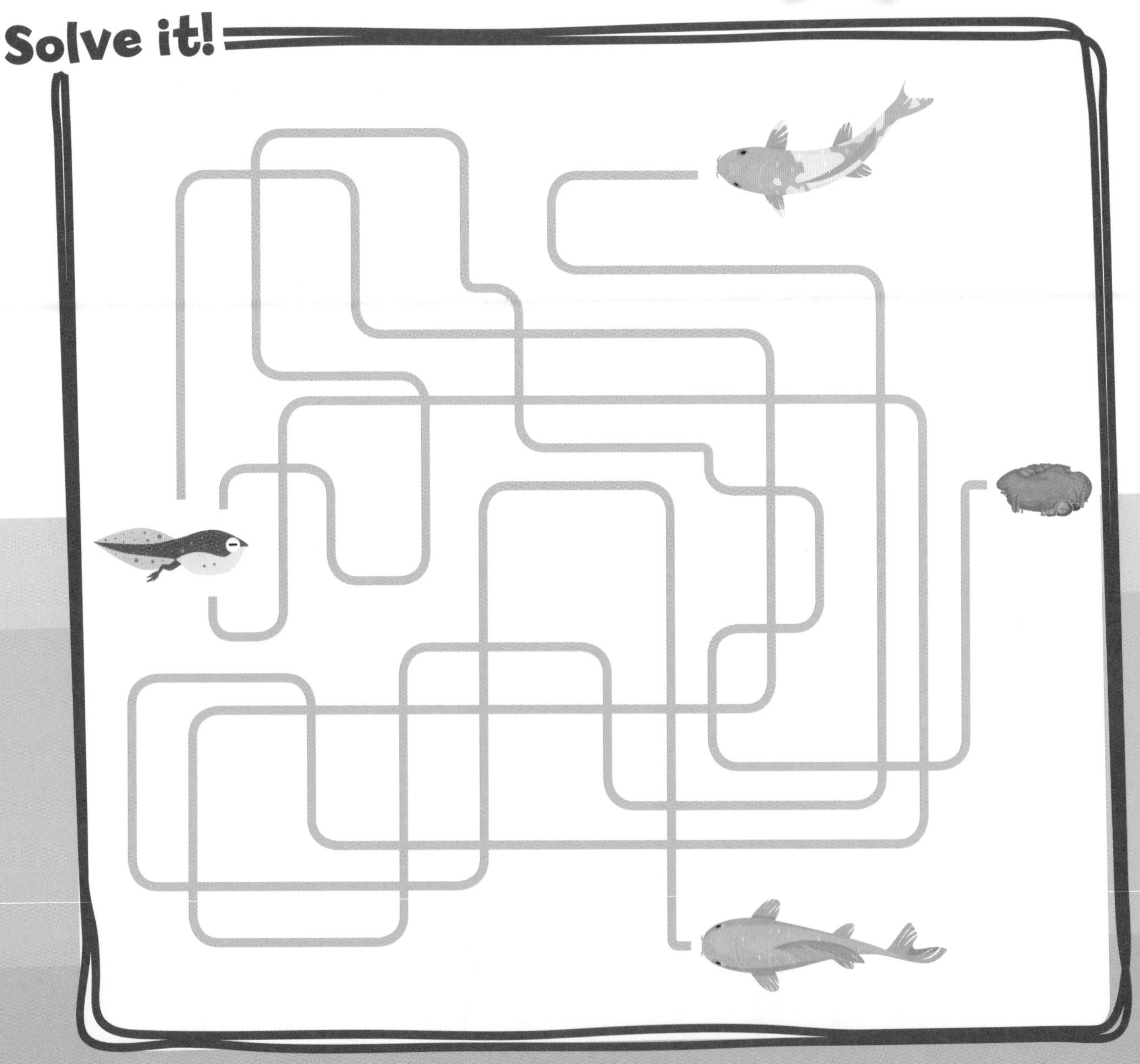

Tadpoles

Spot it!

20 POINTS

Look at the pond pictures.
Can you spot 5 differences?

Solve it!

Lambs like to play games in groups - it's only when they get older that they spend more time alone.

Can you guide this spring lamb through the maze to find its friends!

Spring - reptiles

A slow worm looks like a snake but it's actually a lizard. They can be hard to spot because they are very shy.

Spot it!

35 POINTS

Can you complete this slow worm sudoku puzzle by making sure that the numbers 1 to 6 appear only once in each row, column and box?

6	4	2	5	1	
3					
			4		5
5		4			
					4
	1	6			

Solve it!

1	6	2	4	3	
	3				1
	1		5		
		4		1	
6				5	
			2		

Spring - flowers

There are plenty of flowers to find in the countryside during spring. Can you match the descriptions to the correct flowers?

Solve it!

A

This is one of the first spring flowers to appear, brightening the forest floors with a carpet of bright yellow 'stars'.

B

This is another of the first spring flowers to appear on the woodland floor, forming a carpet of dazzling white flowers.

C

These flowers are a vivid pink/purple colour and are often associated with love and love potions in folklore.

D

These white, pink-tinged flowers are very delicate and fold themselves up during rain or at night. This is thought to be why it is sometimes known as 'Sleeping Beauty'.

E

This tree's flowers look a bit like purple brains, or coral, exploding out of black buds!

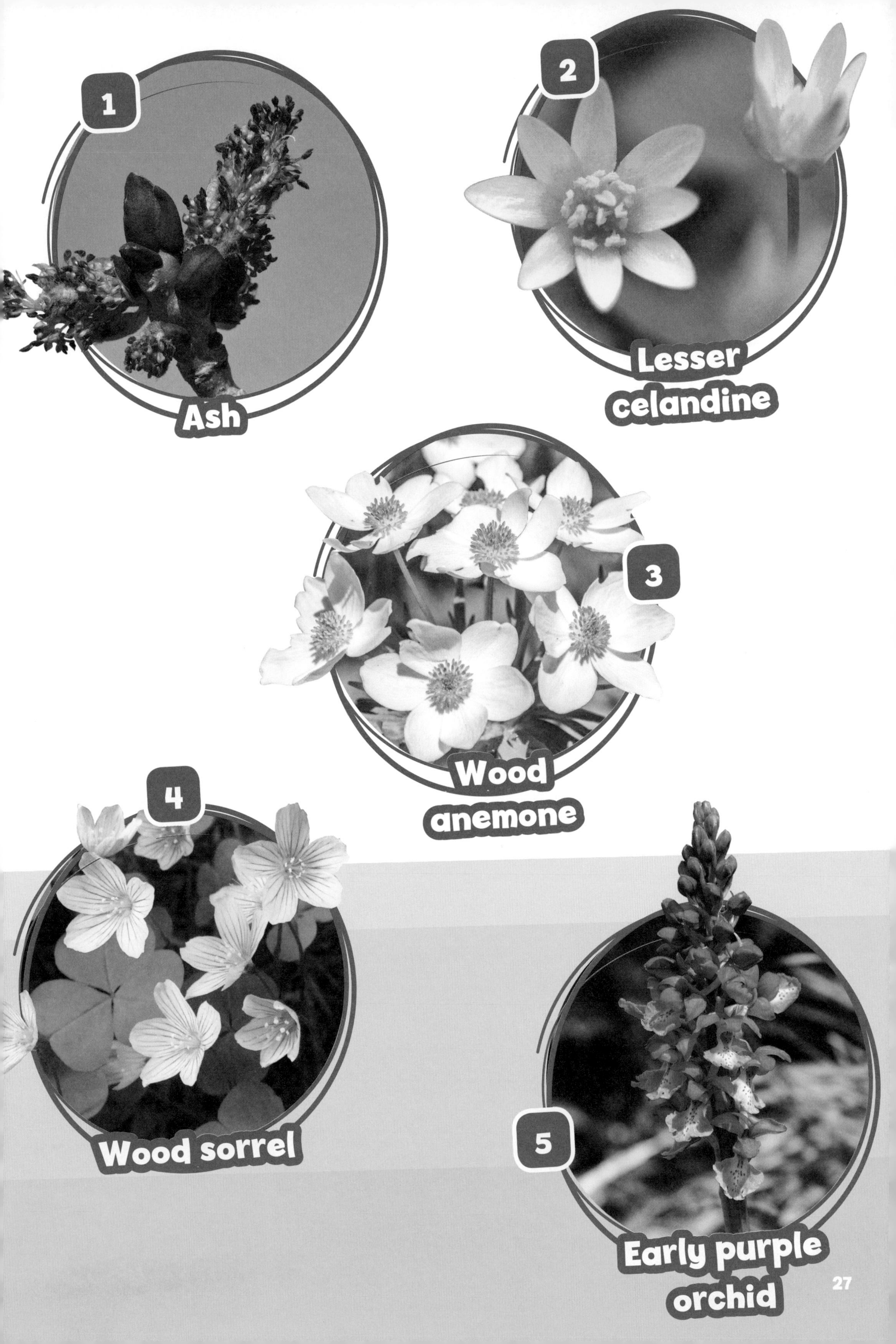
1
Ash
2
Lesser celandine
3
Wood anemone
4
Wood sorrel
5
Early purple orchid

Spring/summer - flowers

Can you answer these quiz questions?

Solve it!

1. Which of the flowers pictured did Medieval people think helped to heal everything from broken bones to ulcers?

2. Which of the flowers pictured was thought to be a charm against evil spirits and was hung above doorways to stop the devil from entering houses?

3. Which of the flowers pictured is often known as 'bacon and eggs' because of the colour of its petals?

Dandelion

Spot it!

○ 10 POINTS

Did you know? The sap inside a dandelion stem makes a great invisible ink – perfect for writing secret messages!

Use the space below to write a message using dandelion sap as ink. The writing will be invisible to begin with. Just leave this book open somewhere warm, and once the sap has dried your secret message should appear!

Write here!

Summer - minibeasts

The Peacock butterfly's name comes from the 'eyes' on its wings, which look similar to those on a peacock's tail.

Can you complete the butterfly below by drawing a symmetrical set of wings? Then colour them in with bright colours.

Peacock butterfly

Spot it! 25 POINTS

Bee

You will probably see plenty of bees buzzing around during summer. Can you help this bee find its way back to the hive?

Solve it!

Summer - leaves

Field maple seeds spin like helicopter propellers as they fall.

Field maple

Spot it!

10 POINTS

Sycamore trees also have leaves that spin when they fall. Look at the Sycamore tree below – it's got a little mixed up! Can you number the pieces to put the picture back in the correct order?

Lime trees have heart-shaped leaves. The common lime was planted so much in towns and parks in the 17th century that it got the name 'common' as a result.

Can you spot the 5 differences between the park photos below?

Lime

Spot it!

20 POINTS

Solve it!

Summer - leaves

Holly fruit ripens in winter but it's glossy leaves are shown throughout the year.

Can you rearrange the letters to form these 4 words that are often associated with holly?

Solve it!

Hint: relating to Christmas.

Hint: something that has leaves all year round.

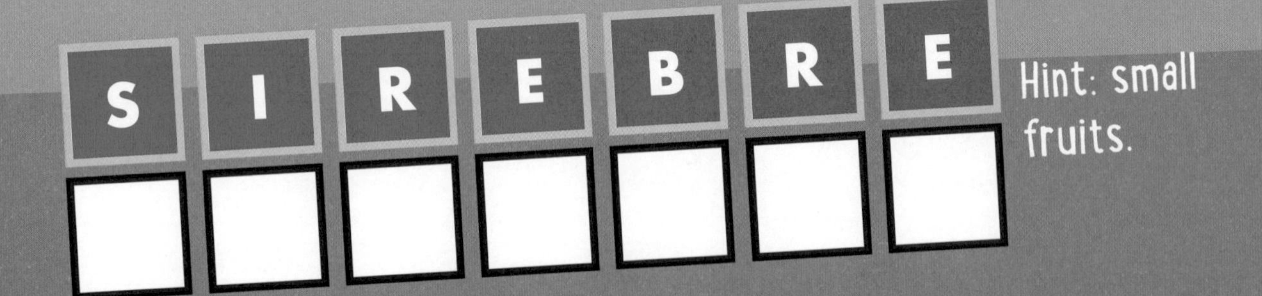

Hint: how holly leaves feel.

Y K P S E I

As you can see, there are many different kinds of leaves you might be able to spot in the countryside during the summer.

Can you match the close-ups below to the picture above?

Summer - bark

Silver birch trees have slim trunks, silver flaky bark and fluttering leaves.

The silver birch tree goes by many other names. Can you find out which of the names below are used for the silver birch and circle them? Hint – there are four.

Betula pendula

Warty birch

Silver tower

Ghost of the forest

Lady of the woods

Arborus redintegrentur

White birch

Paper tree

Solve it!

Older sweet chestnuts are usually massive, with many having huge hollow trunks that several people can fit into at once!

Find the biggest, oldest looking tree that you can, then answer the questions below.

Write here!

How old do you think this tree is?

What are some of the most amazing things that this tree might have seen during its long lifetime?

If this tree could talk, what do you think it would say to you?

Fungi

You will find fungi and mushrooms in most wooded areas. They are great to look at but can be very poisonous so please don't touch any or you could get very ill.

Chicken of the woods

Spot it!

40 POINTS

This unusual-looking fungus is often found on oak trees.

Can you complete the fungi sudoku puzzles by making sure that the numbers 1 to 6 appear only once in each row, column and box?

5	4	6	1		2
		2			4
	5				
				5	
1			3		
2			6		

2	4	6	5	3	
	5				
1			2		
		2			5
				6	
	1		4		

Solve it!

King Alfred's cakes is a fungus where insects and other small animals make their home.

Can you guide this insect through the maze to find the way back to its home inside the fungus?

Solve it!

Fungi

Chanterelle

Inkcap

Jelly ear

Orange peel

Waxcap

Yellow brain

There are many different types of fungi to spot when exploring the countryside. How many of the fungi listed on the opposite page can you discover in the wild?

How many of them can you find in the wordsearch below?

t	y	o	b	p	f	z	m	t	g	x	i	i
j	e	p	y	u	n	g	r	a	u	r	x	a
e	l	r	k	l	s	t	m	r	r	g	a	p
l	l	r	l	a	r	u	l	u	t	r	a	d
l	o	c	h	a	n	t	e	r	e	l	l	e
y	w	m	t	y	m	r	w	a	x	c	a	p
e	b	p	m	d	x	e	n	a	x	e	r	u
a	r	u	z	k	g	b	i	r	o	j	a	k
r	a	c	p	l	s	a	i	n	k	c	a	p
l	i	o	t	u	j	t	s	t	e	d	q	k
t	n	y	p	u	f	f	b	a	l	l	c	u
t	u	l	m	a	w	b	x	c	r	c	o	e
o	r	a	n	g	e	p	e	e	l	k	a	x

Solve it!

Fly agaric

Spot it!

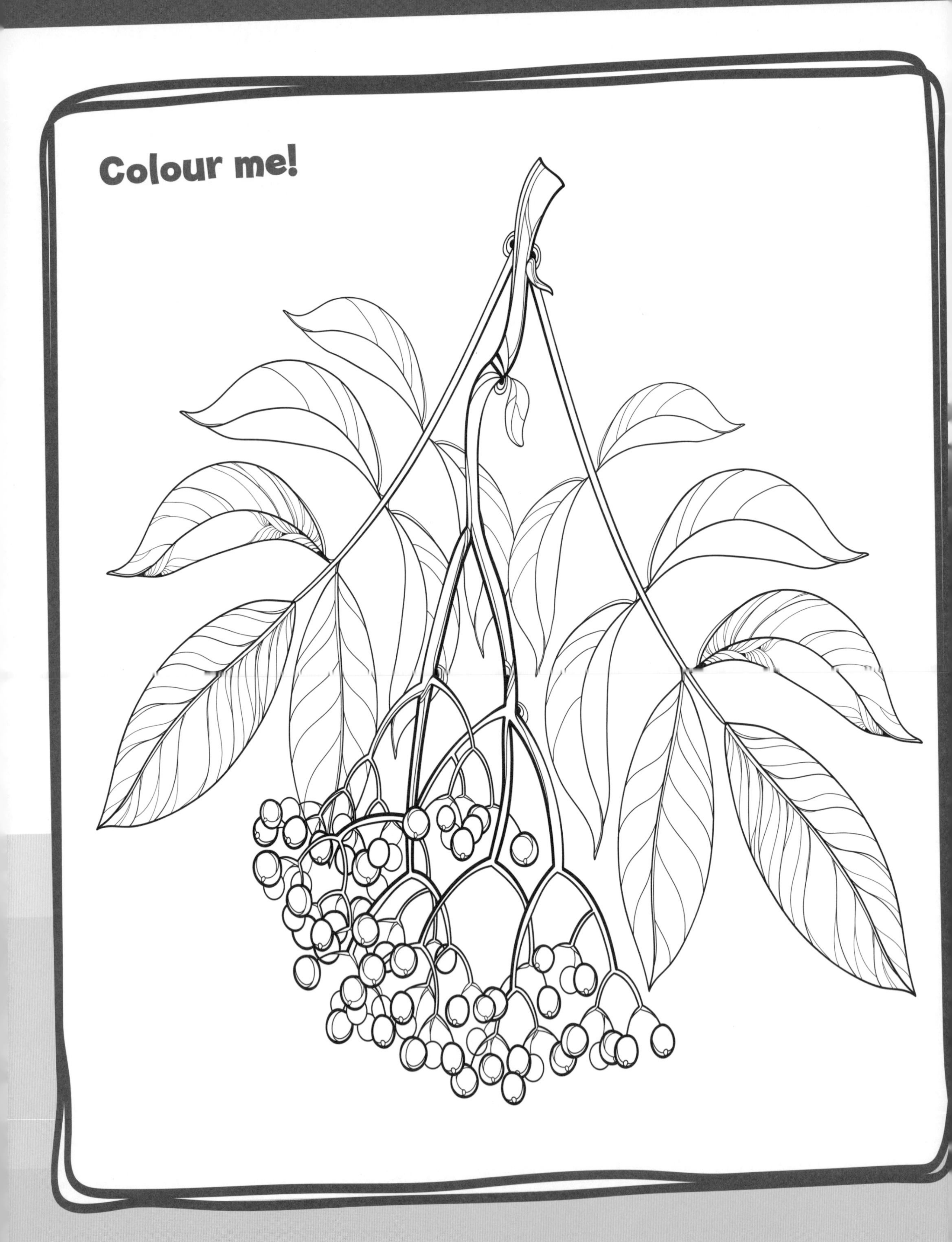
Colour me!

Look at the drawing of the berries on the left.
Can you guess which berry it is?
Add colour and bring the image to life.

Autumn - mammals

Stags and hedgehogs are only some of the animals you might find in the countryside.

Can you rearrange the letters in the word wheels to reveal the names of other mammals you might see in the countryside during the autumn?

Stag

Spot it!

30 POINTS

Solve it!

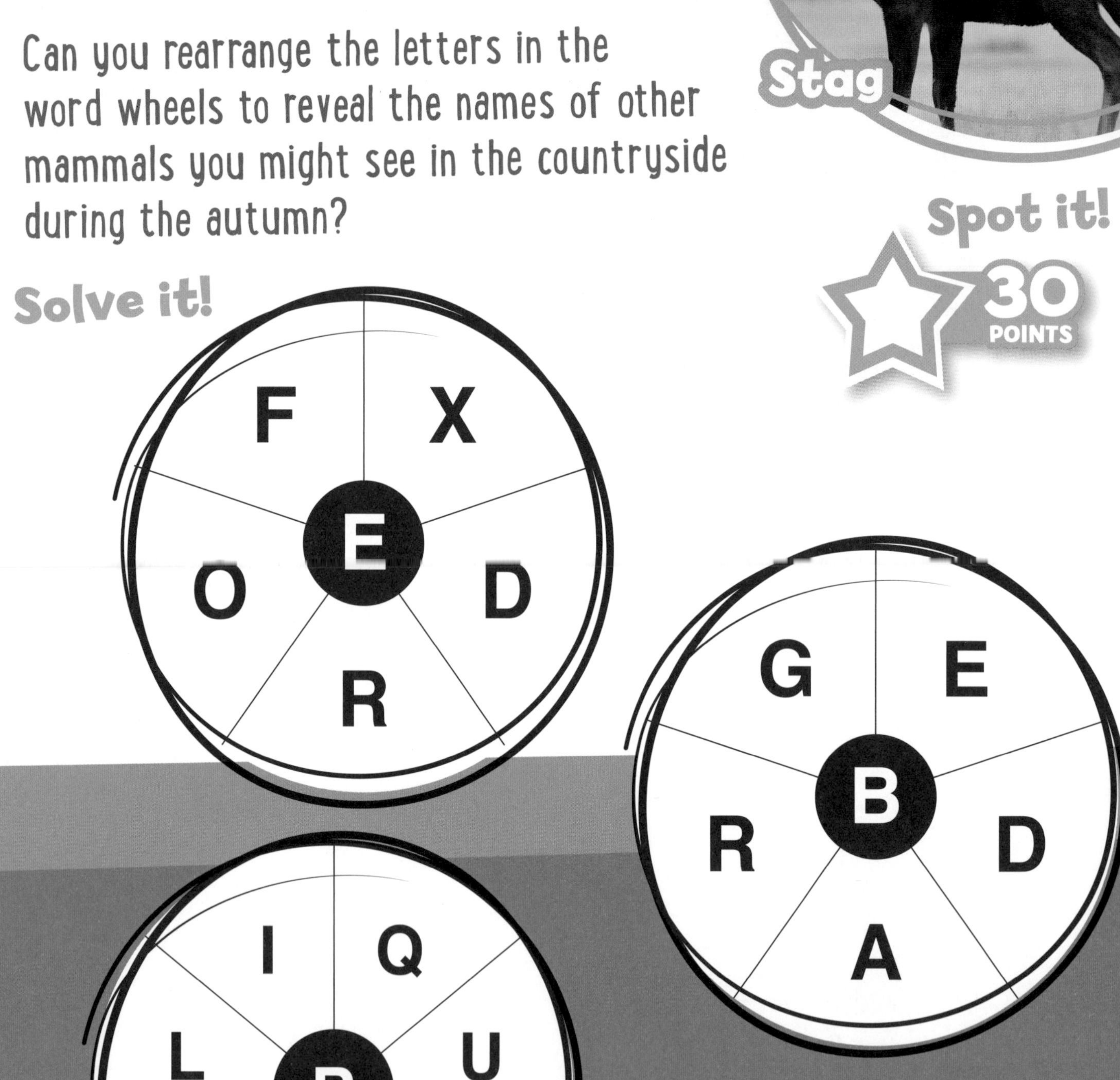

Hedgehogs feast throughout early autumn to store up enough energy to hibernate through the winter. You're most likely to see a hedgehog after dark.

Can you answer the quiz questions below all about the moon?

1 There is only one month that can occur without a full moon - which month is it?

2 In which month of the year is the full moon also known as the 'Harvest Moon', 'Corn Moon', or 'Barley Moon'?

3 Which planet in our solar system has the most known moons? (With a grand total of over 60 moons!)

Solve it!

Full moon

Spot it!

10 POINTS

In early autumn male spiders start scurrying around looking for a mate, so this is why you might suddenly notice more of them around your house at this time of year.

Can you spot the 5 differences between the spiderweb photos below?

Solve it!

Autumn - spooky

Crows can look especially spooky when they are flying through the autumn mist.

This crow got lost in the mist and needs to find its way back to its nest. Can you help it through the maze?

Freshly fallen snow is brilliant for playing in! You can make footprints or build a snowman.

If you could design your own snowman, what would it look like?

Design your snowman here!

Winter - cold

Snowflakes often form patterns that have 3 lines of symmetry.

Can you draw the rest of the snowflake and add the lines of symmetry?

Draw here!

Icicles

Look out for icicles hanging from tree branches in cold, frosty woods.

Can you rearrange the letters to form these 4 words that are often associated with cold weather?

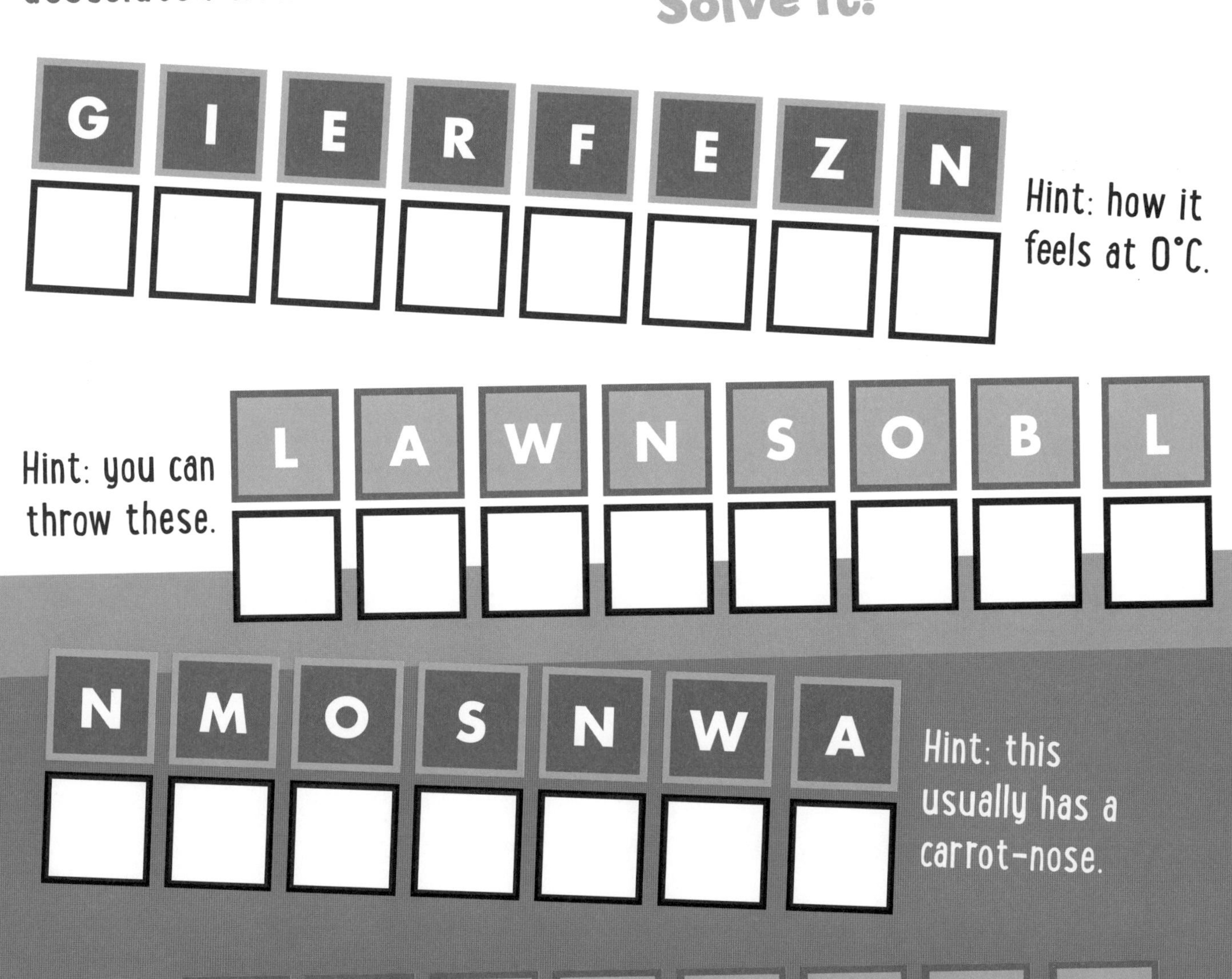

Hint: how ice feels under your feet.

Y E P I S L P R

Winter - tracks

Look out for the tracks of badgers, deer, squirrels and even your own welly footprints. What other tracks can you see? Can you match the footprints to the animals below?

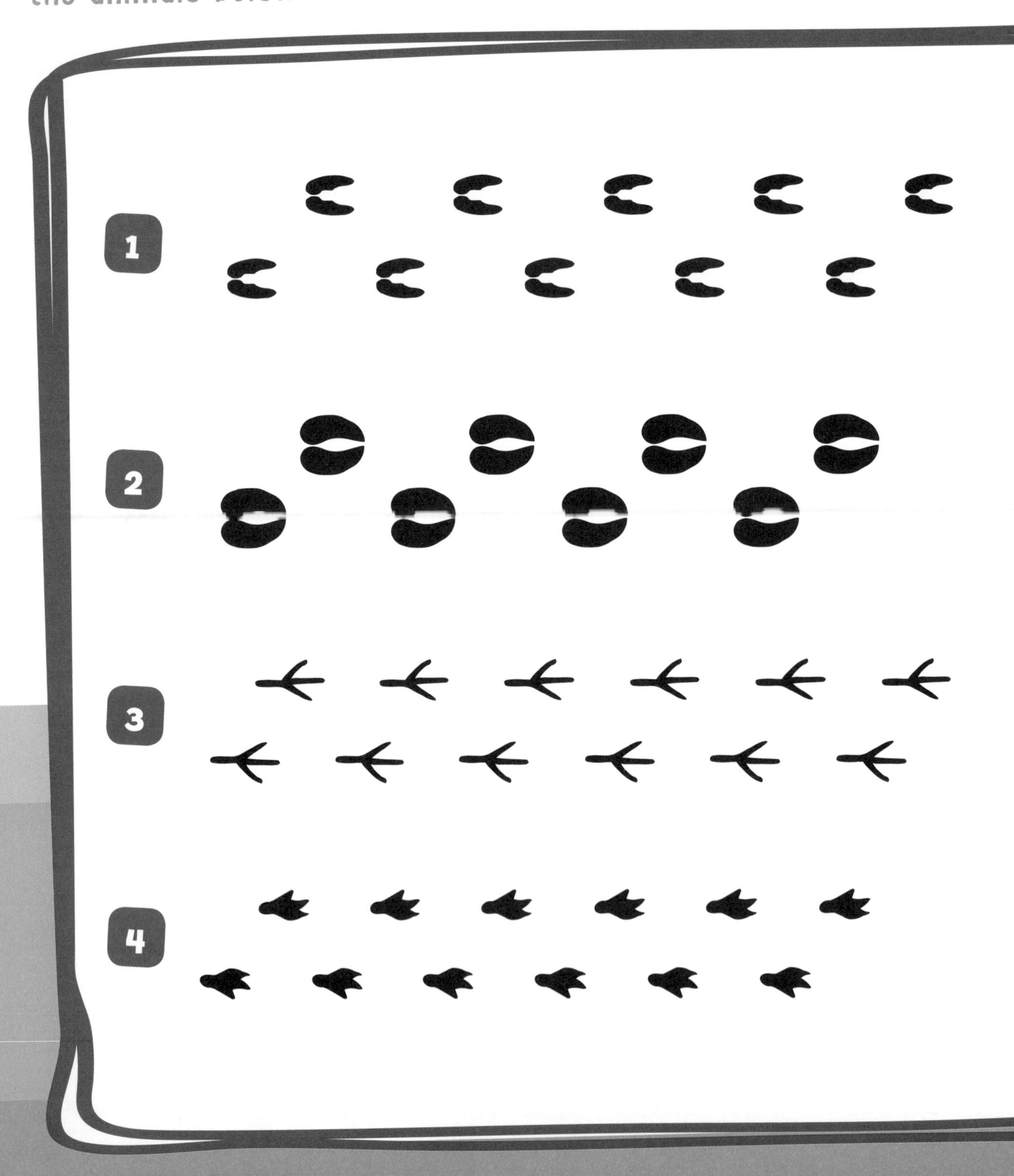

Wellies

Spot it!

5 POINTS

Deer

Crow

Sheep

Squirrel

Animal tracks

Spot it!

25 POINTS

Winter - twigs

Never mind the cold, wrap yourself up and see how many of these winter twigs you can find.

Ash

Ash twigs are grey, with large, velvety-black pointy buds. Did you know the ash tree belongs to the olive family?

Spot it!

10 POINTS

Beech

Beech twigs often grow in a zig-zag shape.

Spot it!

10 POINTS

Horse chestnut

In winter, the ends of horse chestnut twigs have small sticky buds on them.

Spot it!

10 POINTS

Field maple

The field maple is the only maple tree that is native to the UK.

Spot it!

10 POINTS

Landscapes and features

Woodland

Woods are a great place to go for a walk. See how many different types of tree you can spot while you're there.

Spot it! 10 POINTS

See if you can make it from one side of the woodland to the other by finding your way through this maze...

Solve it!

Landscapes and features

Spot it!

◯ 10 POINTS

The UK countryside is packed with rivers, hills and mountains. If you want to have a splash in some streams, remember to wear your wellies! If you could design your own wellies, what would they look like?

Colour me!

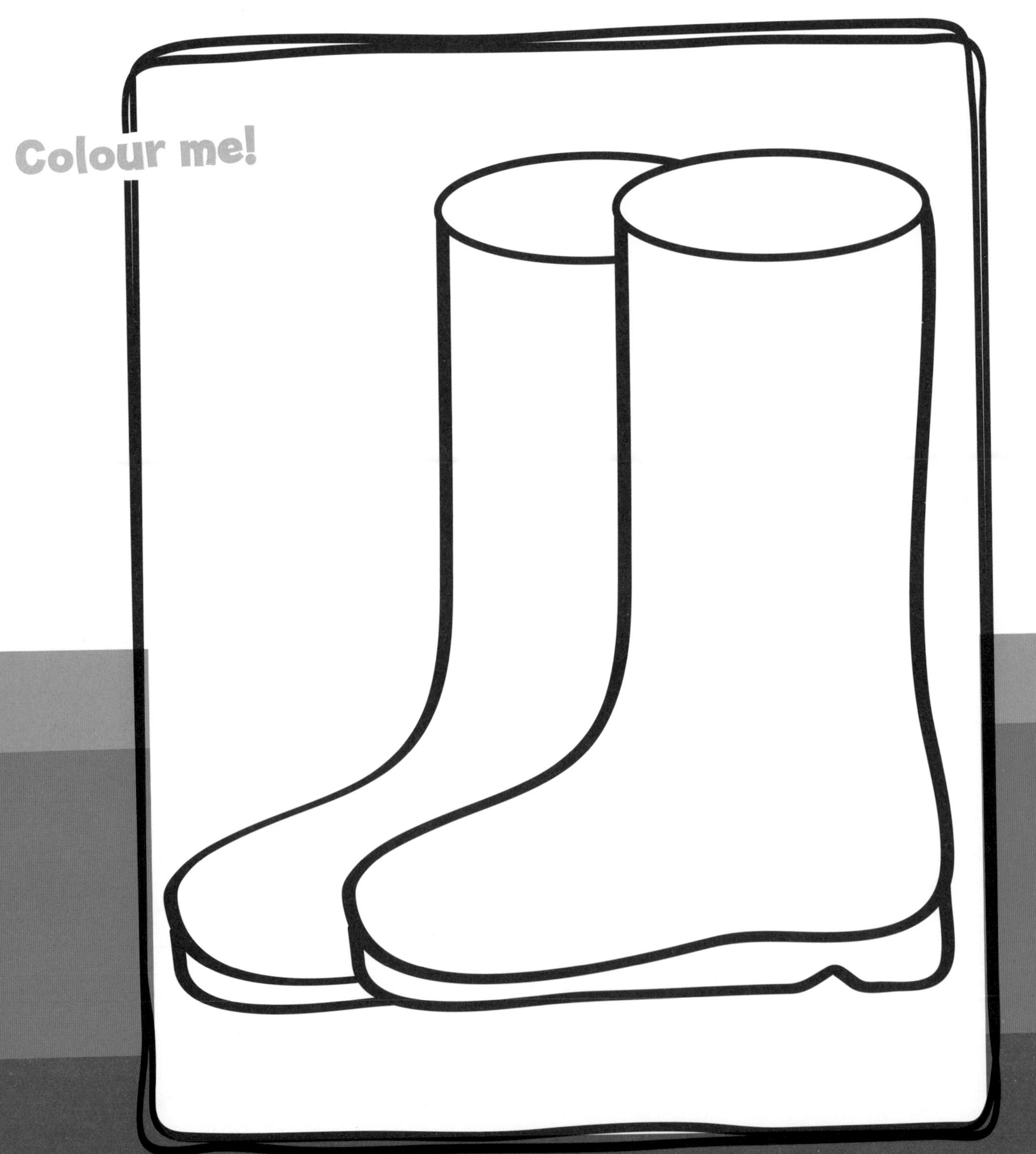

'The 3 Peaks' are the highest mountains in Scotland, England and Wales. Can you place the name of each peak and its height in the correct location?

Solve it!

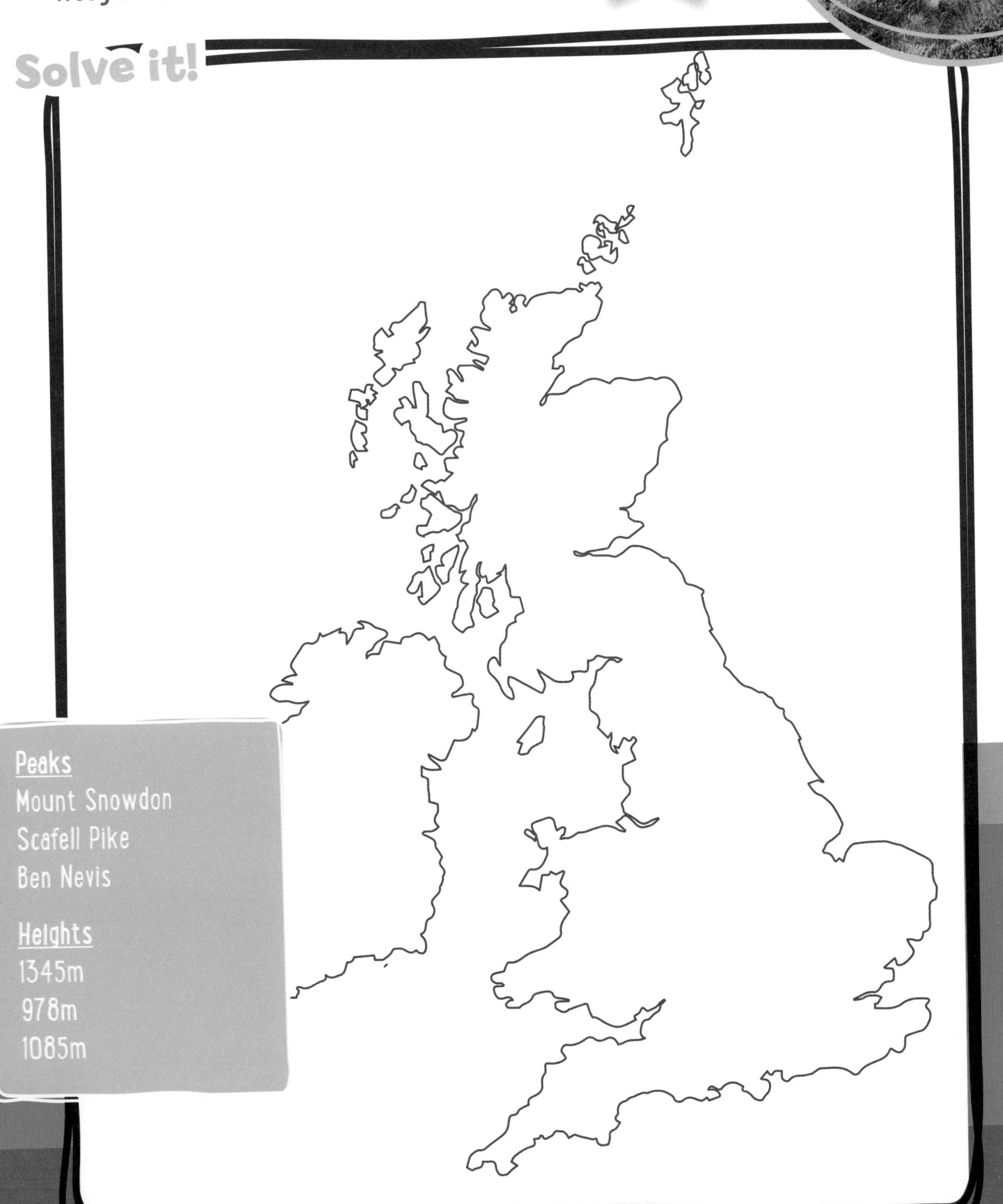

Peaks
Mount Snowdon
Scafell Pike
Ben Nevis

Heights
1345m
978m
1085m

Landscapes and features

Wetlands are an important habitat for plants and birds.

Can you rearrange the letters in the word wheels to reveal the names of these 3 kinds of wetland?

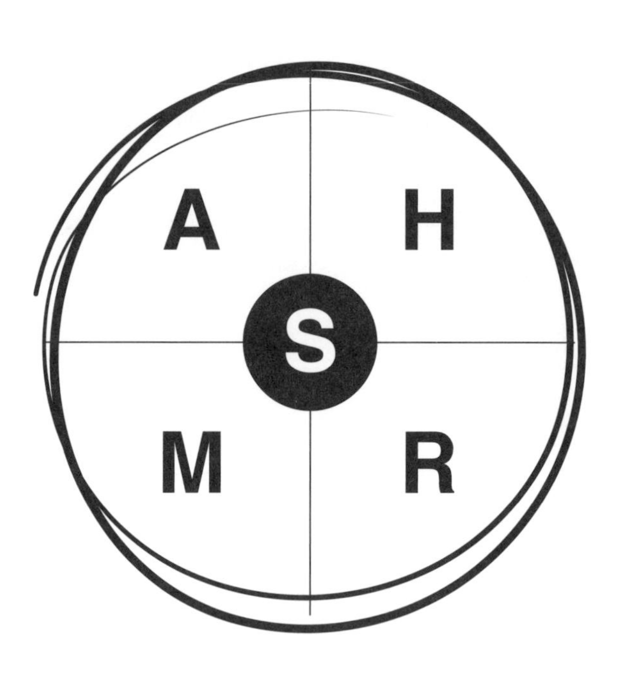

Solve it!

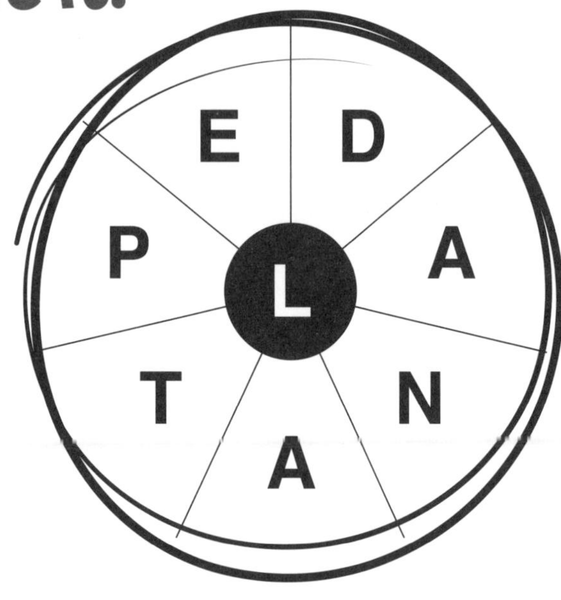

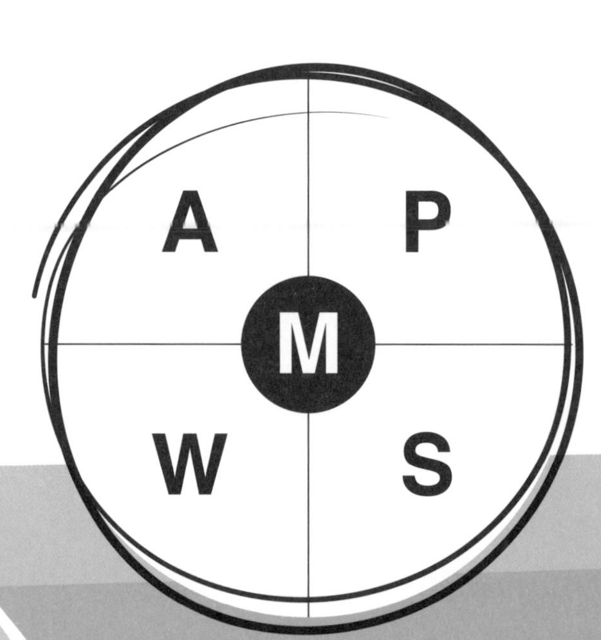

Wetland

Spot it!

Your experience

What fun you've had in the countryside!

Answer the questions below to record your *i-SPY In the Countryside* experience.

Draw or write here!

What is your favourite thing about being in the countryside?

What was the most difficult thing to spot?

What was the best thing you spotted?

Solutions

Page 7

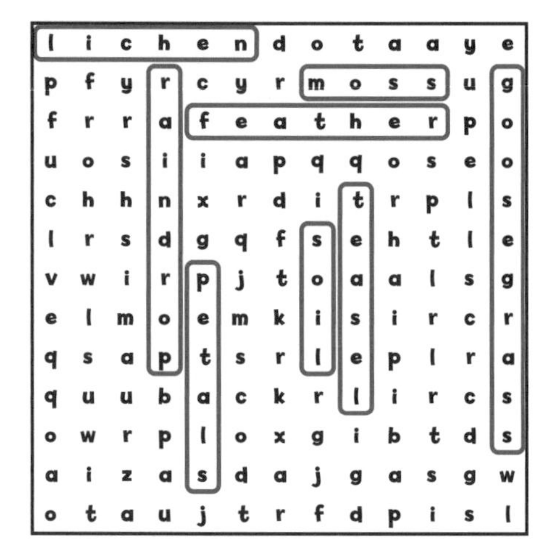

Page 8

HOOTING
CHIRPING
RIBBITING

Page 10

Page 12

BLACKCURRANT
RASPBERRY
STRAWBERRY

Page 21

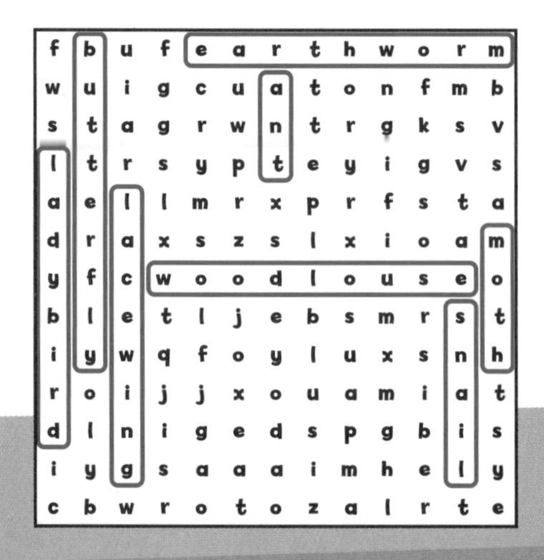

Page 22

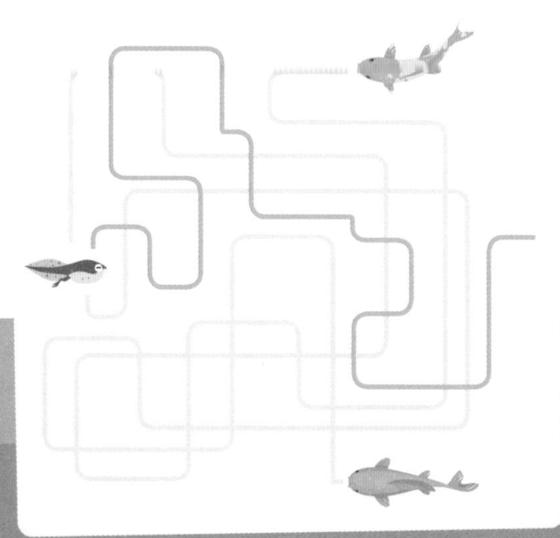

Page 23

Page 24

Page 25

6	4	2	5	1	3
3	5	1	2	4	6
1	6	3	4	2	5
5	2	4	6	3	1
2	3	5	1	6	4
4	1	6	3	5	2

1	6	2	4	3	5
4	3	5	6	2	1
3	1	6	5	4	2
2	5	4	3	1	6
6	2	3	1	5	4
5	4	1	2	6	3

Pages 26 - 27

A - 2, Lesser celandine
B - 3, Wood anemone
C - 5, Early purple orchid
D - 4, Wood sorrel
E - 1, Ash

Page 28

1 - Bugle
2 - Wood avens
3 - Bird's-foot trefoil

Page 31

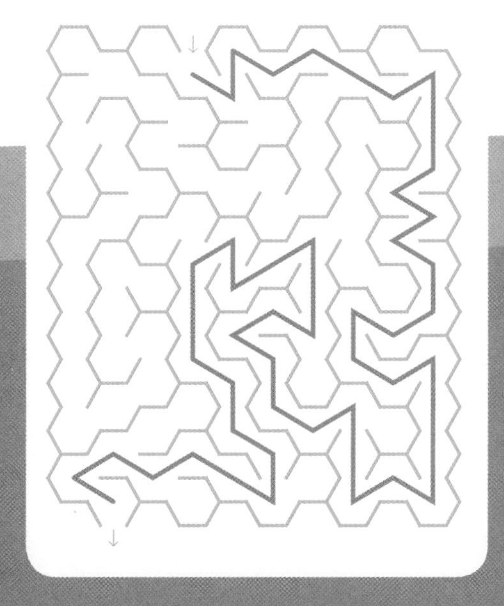

Page 32

2 5 1 4 3

Solutions

Page 33

Page 34

FESTIVE
EVERGREEN
BERRIES
SPIKEY

Page 35

A – Horse chestnut
B – Oak
C – Rowan
D – Hazel

Page 36

Betula pendula
Warty birch
Lady of the woods
White birch

Page 38

2	4	6	5	3	1
3	5	1	6	2	4
1	3	5	2	4	6
4	6	2	3	1	5
5	2	4	1	6	3
6	1	3	4	5	2

5	4	6	1	3	2
3	1	2	5	6	4
4	5	3	2	1	6
6	2	1	4	5	3
1	6	4	3	2	5
2	3	5	6	4	1

Page 39

Page 41

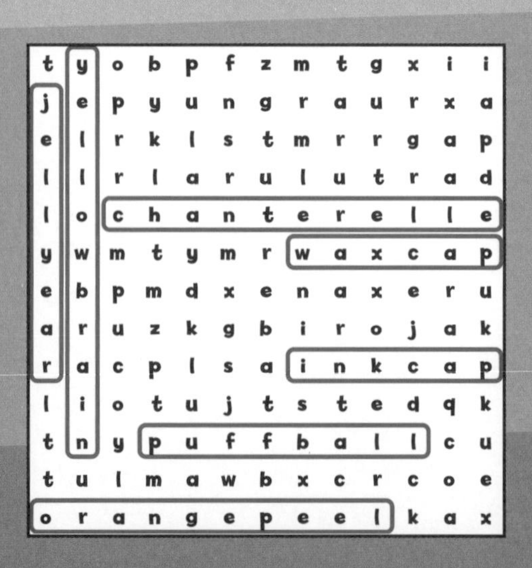

t	y	o	b	p	f	z	m	t	g	x	i	i
j	e	p	y	u	n	g	r	a	u	r	x	a
e	l	r	k	l	s	t	m	r	r	g	a	p
l	l	r	l	a	r	u	l	u	t	r	a	d
l	o	c	h	a	n	t	e	r	e	l	l	e
y	w	m	t	y	m	r	w	a	x	c	a	p
e	b	p	m	d	x	e	n	a	x	e	r	u
a	r	u	z	k	g	b	i	r	o	j	a	k
r	a	c	p	l	s	a	i	n	k	c	a	p
l	i	o	t	u	j	t	s	t	e	d	q	k
t	n	y	p	u	f	f	b	a	l	l	c	u
t	u	l	m	a	w	b	x	c	r	c	o	e
o	r	a	n	g	e	p	e	e	l	k	a	x

Page 43

Elderberry

Page 44

RED FOX
BADGER
SQUIRREL

Page 46

1 – February
2 – September
3 – Jupiter

Page 47

Page 48

Page 50

Page 51

FREEZING
SNOWBALL
SNOWMAN
SLIPPERY

Page 52

1 – Sheep
2 – Deer
3 – Crow
4 – Squirrel

Page 57

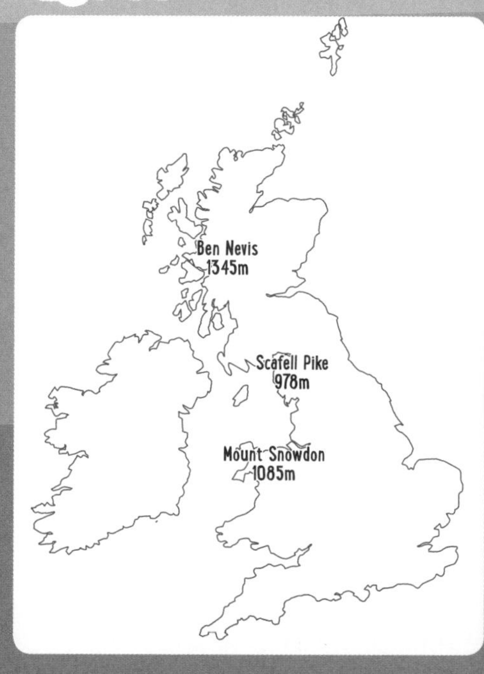

Page 58

MARSH
PEATLAND
SWAMP

Certificate

This certificate is awarded to

....

Congratulations on completing

i-SPY In the Countryside Activity Book

My score:

Date: ....

Keep on spotting!
Keep on solving!